# JAMES
## and the
# RAIN

## by KARLA KUSKIN

The author-artist of ROAR AND MORE (see back panel) has written a second book which is as gay and funny as her first. In addition to being a delightfully merry story-poem, JAMES AND THE RAIN is also an elementary and simple counting book for the youngest child.

*"What do you do in the rain?" said James. "Do you have any excellent rainy day games?"*

With these words James questioned the birds and animals he met on his amble under the wet gray sky. One cow, two ducks, three toads, four birds—they all had their own special way of enjoying the shower. And they all joined James on his stroll.

They dodged drops and scuddled puddles (for an explanation of "to scuddle" read the story), and caught rain drops on their tongues. After all the fun and exercise they were happy to take the advice of the eight cats, who enjoyed the rain in their own particular manner.

Children who are learning to count, or who are proud of their counting talent, will delight in checking the number of cats, ducks, toads, birds, dogs, etc., in each of the deft and appealing pictures.

# James and the Rain

HARPER & ROW, PUBLISHERS
New York, Evanston, and London

by
## Karla Kuskin

James pressed his nose against the pane
And saw a million drops of rain
The earth was wet
The sky was gray
It looked like it would rain all day.

James had a very yellow coat
That buttoned to his chin
He had a pair of rubber boots
To tuck his trousers in
He took a big umbrella
From the big umbrella stand
He buttoned up his yellow coat
And looked extremely grand
He opened his umbrella
With the handle made of cane
He pulled his yellow hat down tight
And stepped into the rain.

Out in a meadow of clover and grain
A cow munched her lunch
And gazed at the rain.
"What do you do in the rain?" said James
"Do you have any excellent rainy day games?"

"I do," said the cow
"For I love the rain
"And the sound it makes on the leaves and grain
"I always stand under a very large tree
"And let the rain fall on the leaves and me."
Then James and the cow stood side by side
And the rain came down
On the cow's brown hide.

"Cow," said James
"If I'm not wrong
"It might be nice if we strolled along."

so they strolled along till they met two ducks...

"What do you do in the rain?" said James

"Do you have any excellent rainy day games?"

"We do," snapped the ducks

In small short quacks

"We love the rain as it falls on our backs

"We flap our feathers

"And flitter around

"Making a rackety quackety sound."

Then all of them flittered

And gave loud quacks

And the rain rained down on all of their backs.

"Ducks," mooed the cow

"If I'm not wrong

"It might be nice if we strolled along."

so they strolled along till they met three toads...

   "What do you do in the rain?" said James

   "Do you have any excellent rainy day games?"

"We love the rain," croaked the three fat toads

"And the puddles of mud that it makes in the roads

"From puddle to puddle we scuddle and jump

"We land in the mud with a thud and a thump

"Come jump with us all."

So they all of them jumped

They all of them scuddled

And all of them thumped.

(a scuddle is the short sticky run from one

mud puddle to the next)

"Toads," quacked the ducks
"If we're not wrong
"It might be nice if we strolled along."

so they strolled along till they met four birds...

"What do you do in the rain?" said James

"Do you have any excellent rainy day games?"

"Well," said the birds
"When it rains we soar
"Up to the clouds and a little bit more
"We seek and we search
"Soaking our skins
"To try to find out where the rain begins."
So all of them tried to soar to the sky
But only the birds got a little bit high.

"Birds," croaked the toads

"If we're not wrong

"It might be nice if we strolled along."

so they strolled along till they met five dogs...

   "What do you do in the rain?" said James

   "Do you have any excellent rainy day games?"

"Rowf," said the dogs and began to bark
"We love the rain
"It's a marvelous lark
"We crash and we splash and we slip on stones
"We scurry and hurry to bury our bones
"We stick out our tongues as we scamper around
"And drink down the rain with a glunking sound."
(glunk is the sound everybody makes
when they drink in a hurry. You glunk)
So all of them stuck their tongues way out
And the rain was so cold that they had to shout.

"Dogs," chirped the birds
"If we're not wrong
"It might be nice if we strolled along."

so they strolled along till they met six rabbits ...
    "What do you do in the rain?" said James
    "Do you have any excellent rainy day games?"

"Oh," said the rabbits and nibbled their lettuce
"We like the rain if it doesn't wet us
"We race in the rain right out of our hutches
"We run so fast that the rain can't touch us."
So everyone raced with their might and main
Trying to dodge the drops of rain
(but nobody did).

Then the dogs barked
"Rabbits, if we're not wrong
"It might be nice if we strolled along."

so they strolled along till they met seven mice...
 "What do you do in the rain?" said James
 "Do you have any excellent rainy day games?"

"Oh," squeaked the mice
Who were terribly shy
"We like the rain
"If our ears stay dry
"We pick red flowers
"Out of their beds
"And wear them as hats
"To cover our heads."
Then they all picked flowers just like the mice
And wore them as hats and looked very nice.

Then the rabbits peeped
"Mice, if we're not wrong
"It might be nice if we strolled along."

so they strolled along till they met eight cats . . .

"What do you do in the rain?" said James

"Do you have any excellent rainy day games?"

"Meow," mewed the cats
"We like the rain
"And the sound that it makes
  on the window pane
"But best of all
"As the wind howls higher
"We like to sit by a roaring fire."

So they went inside and sat by the fire
The rain came down
And the wind howled higher
And that is the end
It rained and it poured
They all fell asleep
And all of them snored.

THE END